Rise Sally Rise

Great Singing Games for Children

a companion to the CD ❖ 2014 edition
edited by Peter and Mary Alice Amidon

❖ NEW ENGLAND DANCING MASTERS ❖

Rise Sally Rise

info@dancingmasters.com
www.dancingmasters.com

Additional copies of this book may be ordered from the above address.

edited by
Peter & Mary Alice Amidon
20 Willow Street, Brattleboro, VT 05301
802-257-1006 • amidonpeter@gmail.com • www.amidonmusic.com

This collection was first published in 1992 with the title "Jump Jim Joe".

Please send us your comments and suggestions.

Photos by Jim Powers

Cover design, diagrams, and text typesetting by Nicky Dumont

Music transcriptions by Peter Amidon

ISBN: 978-0-9906716-0-2

Other singing games collections from New England Dancing Masters:

Rise Sally Rise - Great Singing Games for Children
CD companion to this book. Recordings of all of the singing games in the book
performed by Peter, Mary Alice, Sam and Stefan Amidon.

Down in the Valley - More Great Singing Games for Children
edited by Andy Davis, Peter Amidon and Mary Alice Amidon, this is another treasure
trove of time-tested singing games for children. Book and companion CD.

*I'm Growing Up - Fingerplays, Action Songs, Singing Games
and Stories for Young Children*
A set of book/CD/DVD, edited by Mary Alice Amidon and Andy Davis, this includes
54 music/movement activities for children from pre-school to 2nd grade.

You can get a complete listing of all the New England Dancing Masters' dance
and singing games collections (books, CDs, DVDs) by visiting:

www.dancingmasters.com

Contents

Original Introduction

This collection includes but a handful of the countless traditional singing games that have been danced, sung and passed on by generations of children throughout the U.S. and the British Isles. The purpose of this collection is to make these singing games more accessible to anyone who works with children. In our work in many of the small rural elementary schools in Vermont and New Hampshire we have found the children to have a very limited repertoire of singing games. Some of the singing games we teach in schools become part of the playground culture. Others become part of a repertoire of dances that are shared by the children and teacher in a classroom. Singing games have always been an integral part of our music teaching. The singing games in this collection, and others that you can find, can be an important part of developing a dancing tradition in your school or community. They can also enrich the repertoire of a dance caller who leads community dances for mixed ages. These singing games are mostly from the Anglo American and African American traditions.

There's an old saying from Zimbabwe: If you can talk you can sing. If you can walk you can dance.

Peter and Mary Alice Amidon, 1992

Introduction to the 2014 edition

After the initial success of 'Chimes of Dunkirk - Great Dances for Children' which Andy Davis, Mary Cay Brass and I published in 1991, my wife and partner Mary Alice Amidon and I put together a collection of our favorite singing games gleaned from workshops, community dances, Pinewoods Family Week dance leaders, friends, colleagues, printed dance collections and courses we took on traditional dance and song.   We titled it after the singing game that, at the time, we found the most universal: Jump Jim Joe. Since then we have learned about Jump Jim Joe's complicated ancestry (see Jump Jim Joe notes). After years of discussions between Andy, Mary Cay, Mary Alice and myself, and with many other music/dance educator colleagues, Mary Alice and I decided to leave the Jump Jim Joe singing game in the collection, but to rename the collection with lyrics from the classic singing game Little Sally Walker: "Rise Sally Rise".

Although we have otherwise left much of the book as it was in the original 1992 edition, here are a few other changes we have made:

- improved the clarity of the dance instructions.
- updated teaching tips.
- occasionally modified a singing game to reflect the way we teach it now.
- made the written music reflect more closely our version of the melody.
- added chords to the singing game tunes where appropriate.

The companion recording will have two replacement cuts of music: we are using the 'Alabama Gal' recording that we have been using for 'Chimes of Dunkirk', and the 'Noble Duke of York' recording that we made for our New England Dancing Masters 'Alabama Gal' book/CD/DVD (published by GIA). That gives you the choice of doing these two singing games either a cappella or to the recorded music of a great dance band.

Revisiting this collection has been a reminder to us of the natural grace and beauty of singing games that children have passed on to each other across generations. We hope that this collection helps keep these traditions alive.

Peter Amidon, 2014

Dancing in the Classroom

Here are some tips for teachers on how to make dancing a regular part of classroom life:

Clear out a dancing space. Be creative and bold, making the space as long and wide as possible. With clear assignments and some practice your class should be able to clear the room in less than a minute.

Develop a classroom repertoire that is varied, including *dances as well as singing games. Dance with your students, but also encourage them to dance without you. Combine two or more classes together for a dance party. Do a dance unit with the physical education teacher where you work together with combined classes in the gymnasium. Go to the community dancing events in your area, bringing your students if possible. Invite a traditional dance teacher to your school as an artist-in-residence to teach singing games and dances to the teachers and students. Such a residency can culminate in an evening of dancing for the school and surrounding community.

Most importantly, make these singing games your own. Don't be afraid to modify a singing game to meet the needs of your students. Soon the children will be taking the singing games out onto the playground, and they will be asking you to dance every day. You will know your class has reached dance heaven when you can say: "Listen, I've got some work to do at my desk. Why don't you all clear the room and have a dance."

*For the purposes of this section, 'dances' refers to the whole body of dances in longways, circle and square formations that require live or recorded instrumental music accompaniment (as distinct from singing games) such as found in the new England Dancing Masters collections *Chimes of Dunkirk, Listen to the Mockingbird* and *Sashay the Donut*.

Choosing Leaders and Partners

Most of the singing games require choosing a Leader: the person who leads through one turn of the game. Choosing the second and successive Leaders is usually built into the game. Children left on their own have their own sense of justice about this: the first Leader might be the child whose idea the game was, or simply the first child bold enough to jump in the middle. If a dispute arises they might resort to one of the many counting out chants. One of our favorites is:

Itsa bitsa tootsa la. Falama linka linka la
Falama loo, falama la, Falama linka linka la

where the person on the final "la" is the chosen first Leader.

A quicker way is to have one person spin around while covering their eyes with one hand and pointing with the other; selecting whomever they end up pointing to as the first Leader.

When you are first teaching the singing game you might want to pick the method for choosing the first Leader, or simply choose the first Leader yourself. Eventually it is good to turn this work over to the children, along with the rest of the singing game.

A few of the singing games require partners. Here are a few of the many ways of finding partners:

1) Teacher assigns partners.

2) Form a circle and count off by 'ones and twos'. 'Ones' turn to the right, 'twos' turn to the left. The person facing you is your partner. Or the teacher could go around the circle designating who is dancing with whom.

3) Form a circle. Stretch it into a long skinny oval which will become two lines facing each other. Have the two people at one end take hands with each other, then continue down the line until everyone is partnered up in a longways set.

4) Teach the children how to ask someone to dance. Practice the words together first: "May I please have this dance?" ("Dance please?" for younger children). "Yes, thank you." Then model by asking one of your students to dance, followed by voluntary demonstrations by the students. Soon they will all be able to choose partners at once. If you are dancing gents with ladies (boys with girls) you should make it clear that gents can ask ladies and ladies can ask gents.

Use your own judgment whether or not to have the children have gent/lady partners for the dances. Our solution is to mix gent/lady dancing with 'whomever you want to choose' dancing (which could be a mixture of opposite-gender and same-gender partners). Children who initially resist dancing with opposite-gender partners will soon get used to it if it is done on a regular basis. Children, particularly in school settings, often segregate themselves into same-gender groupings. Traditional singing games and dances can be added to your list of activities that can help break through this polarization.

Acknowledgements

We are indebted to many individuals for sharing their enthusiasm and expertise as well as the singing games themselves. Mary Cay Brass, Andy Davis, Bessie Jones, Maureen Kennedy, John Krumm, Doug Lipman, Jane Miller, Kathy Torrey and Penny Schwartz are just a few of the people who have had an immediate impact on our work with children. We learned many of these singing games for the first time at the Country Dance and Song Society's summer Family Weeks at Pinewoods Camp.

The Singing Games

Alabama Gal

We never thought much of this American playparty game as it appeared in books until we saw it at Pinewoods Camp Family Week danced by children. Since then we have found it to be one of the great all-time singing games for children; they learn it quickly and dance it with gusto.

Come through in a hur - ry, Come through in a hur - ry,
I don't know how, how, I don't know how, how,
I'll show you how, how, I'll show you how, how,
Ain't I rock can - dy, Ain't I rock can - dy,

Come through in a hur - ry, A - la - ba - ma Gal.
I don't know how, how, A - la - ba - ma Gal.
I'll show you how, how, A - la - ba - ma Gal.
Ain't I rock can - dy, A - la - ba - ma Gal.

Formation: Longways set for 6-8 couples.

Come through in a hurry, come through in a hurry,
> First couple sashay down the middle of the set while other dancers stand in place
> clapping to the music.

Come through in a hurry, Alabama Gal.
> First couple sashay back up through the middle to the top of the set while
> other dancers continue clapping.

I don't know how, how, I don't know how, how
> All do right hand turn once around partner and back to place.

I don't know how, how, Alabama Gal.
> All do left hand turn once around partner and back to place.

I'll show you how, how . . . Alabama Gal.
> First couple cast off (turn away from each other and start walking down the
> outside of the set) and others follow behind. First couple meet at the bottom
> of the set and make a two hand arch.

Ain't I rock candy . . . Alabama Gal.
> Second couple meet below the arch, take handy hand with partner
> (lady's left in gent's right) and go under the arch and back to the top of the set.
> All other couples follow, each taking partner's hand before going through the arch.

Repeat the dance with the new first couple.

Notes: We like to have the students skipping through the cast off. That can speed the cast off under
the arches enough that you might be able to do the dance with more than eight couples in a set. Some
students might need to be reminded to bend forward (not backward) when going through the arch.
Do the dance a few times (or for a couple of weeks) a cappella before trying it with the recording.

Bobolinka

For years Kathy Torrey had children's songs and singing games sharing sessions in her East Alstead NH home with others who work with children. We learned 'Bobolinda' (which is called 'Bow Belinda' in older singing games collections) from Kathy at one of these sessions, and somewhere along the way changed it to 'Bobolinka'.

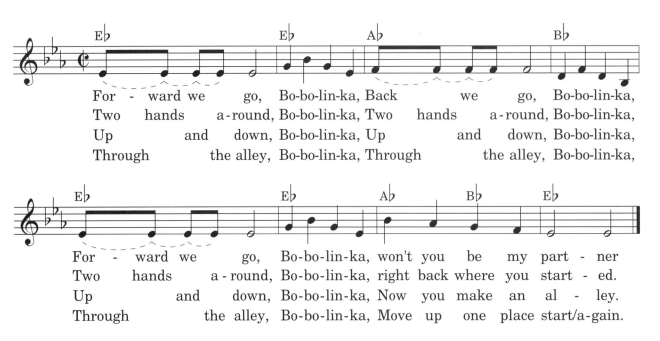

For - ward we go, Bo-bo-lin-ka, Back we go, Bo-bo-lin-ka,
Two hands a - round, Bo-bo-lin-ka, Two hands a - round, Bo-bo-lin-ka,
Up and down, Bo-bo-lin-ka, Up and down, Bo-bo-lin-ka,
Through the alley, Bo-bo-lin-ka, Through the alley, Bo-bo-lin-ka,

For - ward we go, Bo-bo-lin-ka, won't you be my part - ner
Two hands a - round, Bo-bo-lin-ka, right back where you start - ed.
Up and down, Bo-bo-lin-ka, Now you make an al - ley.
Through the alley, Bo-bo-lin-ka, Move up one place start/a-gain.

Formation: Longways set of any number of couples.

Forward we go Bobolinka,

>All walk towards partner, end up close, but not touching.

back we go, Bobolinka,

>All back up to place.

forward we go, Bobolinka, won't you be my partner.

>All go forward and back again.

Two hands around, Bobolinka . . . right back where you started.

>Two hand turn around partner, once, twice or three times around,
>ending up back home at the end of the phrase.

Up and down, Bobolinka, up and down, Bobolinka, up and down, Bobolinka,

>Jump up and down in place.

now you make an alley.

>All except for the First Couple take two hands with partner and raise hands
>to make a tunnel.

**Through the alley, Bobolinka, through the alley, Bobolinka, through the alley,
Bobolinka,**

>First Couple takes one hand with partner and goes all the way down through
>the tunnel to the bottom.

move up one place, start again.

>All drop hands, and move one step up towards the top of the set.

>Repeat the dance with a new First Couple.

Notes: We use this as a first longways dance for young children. You can omit the
arches in **Through the alley** . . . at first, having the children just standing and singing
as the First Couple walks down between the two lines.

Bulldog

We learned this from Mary Cay Brass who learned it from John Krumm who learned it from North Carolina clogger and folklorist Ruth Pershing who learned it from a winter crew member at Farm and Wilderness Camp in Vermont who learned it from some children in an inner city summer camp in Chicago, IL. Ruth has since learned a very similar version from some children in Durham, NC.

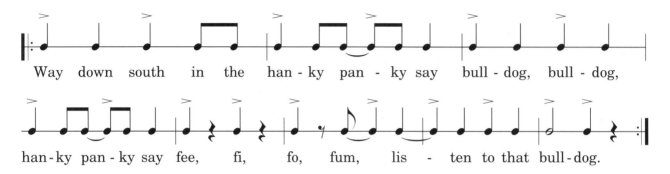

Formation: Circle. Each person's hands are extended to the sides at about waist level. Both palms are up. Each person's right hand is resting on top of the left hand of the neighbor to their right. Each person's left hand is under the right hand of the neighbor to their left.

This is a clapping game of elimination. One person starts by raising their right hand up and over to the left to clap the right hand of the neighbor on their left on the word **Way.** The clapped person then raises their right hand to clap their left neighbor on the word **south.** The clap continues to be passed clockwise to the left around the circle, clapping on the beats as indicated by the accents.

However, the person who would be clapped on the last syllable of the chant (**dog** of **bulldog**) tries to pull their right hand back in time to avoid being clapped. If they succeed in avoiding being clapped, they stay in the game, and the one who missed clapping them is out. If they do get clapped on the last syllable, then they are out of the game and the one who successfully clapped them stays in. The successful one of these two starts the clapping of the next round of the game.

The clapping should stay on the beat of the chant. If someone pulls their hand away before the last syllable they are out. When there are two people left, they face each other, each putting their right hand, palm up, over the other's left hand, and their right hands clap back and forth to the beat of the chant.

Notes: This game is very popular with older elementary children. It helps to have a designated judge to settle disputes. Sometimes there is a natural tendency for the speed of the chant to increase as the game goes on.

Here is a version you can do that eliminates the elimination: have, say, four circles of children doing the game at the same time. Whoever is 'eliminated' in each circle runs over and joins a different circle. The challenge here is to have them change circles fast enough that there is little or no hesitation between rounds of the game.

Circle Round the Zero

Our friend, Orff Schulwerk music educator and musician Maureen Kennedy, collected this singing game from African American children who had been bussed from Roxbury to Hartwell School in Lincoln, MA where Maureen taught music. She says that she has also encountered variants of it in New Bedford, MA and Memphis, TN.

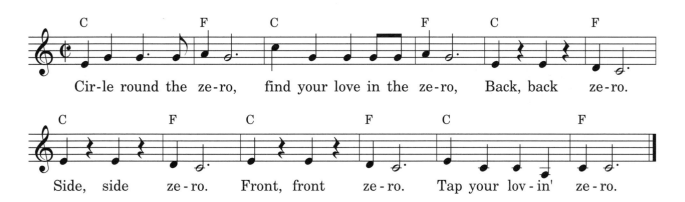

Cir-le round the ze-ro, find your love in the ze-ro, Back, back ze-ro.

Side, side ze-ro. Front, front ze-ro. Tap your lov-in' ze-ro.

Formation: Dancers in a circle, all facing the center and not holding hands. Leader starts on the outside of the circle.

Leader walks clockwise around the outside of the circle as all sing. At **back, back zero,** Leader stops and stands back-to-back with the nearest person. Then, following the words of the song, the Leader stands side-by-side, then front-to-front with that same person, and then taps that person on the shoulder. The two then trade places: the tapped person stepping to the outside of the circle to become the new Leader while the original Leader joins the other children standing in the circle.

Notes: You might remind the children that the Leader does all the moving from back-to-back, side-to-side and front-to-front, while the chosen dancer stands still. Variations include changing the words to *find a friend in the zero.* This can also be done as a snowball dance: the original Leader continues going around after tapping the first person so there are two Leaders at the same time. After they've each tapped someone there are four Leaders, then eight, and so on until everyone is walking around more or less at random. At **back, back zero** everyone scrambles to find someone else to go back to back with. It can get chaotic, but it's fun.

Dinah's Dead

We learned this at the same time that we learned 'When I Was a Baby' in Penny Schultz's workshop on African American singing games.

Formation: Circle, not holding hands. The Leader is in the middle of the circle.

Well Dinah's Dead. **Well how did she die?**
Well she died like this. **Well she died like this.**

The game begins with a simple call and response; the Leader speaking the words in italics, and the rest of the group answering with the other words. On the Leader's word ***this*** the Leader improvises a movement or pose which is imitated by the group when they say their word **this.** This is repeated as the words indicate.

But her sister's still living. **Well where is she living?**
> Simple call and response as before, but with no particular motions.

At this point the Leader and the group all speak and dance together:
She's <u>living</u> <u>in</u> a <u>place</u> <u>called</u> <u>Ten</u>-<u>nes</u>-<u>see</u> <u>with</u> a
> All jump and land with feet crossed, then jump and land with feet uncrossed, then crossed, uncrossed, crossed, uncrossed, crossed, uncrossed each landing happening on the accents of the underlined syllables (this is pretty fast).

short short dress all above her knees
> All mime pulling a dress above the knees

Hands up Tizzie Lizzie, Tennessee, hands down Tizzie Lizzie, Tennessee, turn around Tizzie Lizzie, Tennessee, touch the ground Tizzie Lizzie, Tennessee.
> Everyone does what the words say while dancing to the music.

Well she never went to college . . .
> The Leader spins around covering eyes with one hand while pointing with the other, stopping on the word ***fool.***

Whomever the Leader is pointing to becomes the new Leader.

Notes: This is a wonderful game for older children. Suggesting that children do motions appropriate for school will help discourage overly graphic motions. Encourage the children to pop into the middle quickly when picked to keep the dance moving.

Draw Me A Bucket

We learned this from Bessie Jones. Extensive notes about this and many other singing games passed on by Bessie Jones can be found in her book and recording 'Step It Down'.

Formation: A group of four children standing in a circle all facing into the center.

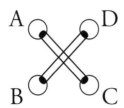

A is holding two hands across with C. B and D are holding each others hands above the arms of A and C.

Draw me a bucket of water for my eldest daughter, there's none in the bunch, we're all out the bunch
> All gently rock forward and back.

you go under Sister Sally.
> D & B raise joined hands (D's left hand and B's right hand) up over C's head and down to the back of C's waist. D and B's other joined hands remain in the middle where they started.

Draw me a bucket of water for my eldest daughter, there's one in the bunch, we're three out the bunch
> All gently rock forward and back.

you go under sister Sally.
> D and B raise the other hand (D's right, B's left) up over A's head and down to the back of A's waist.

Draw me a bucket of water for my eldest daughter, there's two in the bunch, we're two out the bunch
> All gently rock forward and back.

you go under sister Sally.
> A and C raise held hands over B.

Draw me a bucket of water for my eldest daughter, there's two in the bunch, we're two out the bunch
> All gently rock forward and back.

you go under Sister Sally.
> A and C raise remaining hands over D's head. The group is now in a 'basket' formation with all their held hands woven around each others' backs.

Frog in the bucket and I can't get him out. (8X)
All bounce up and down moving circle to the left. On the repeat of the song, the children drop hands to break the basket and rejoin hands in a regular circle and jump the circle around to the left, shaking the frog out of the bucket.

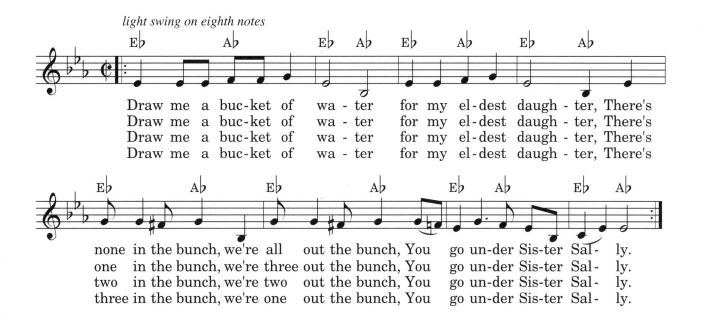

light swing on eighth notes

Draw me a buc-ket of wa - ter for my el-dest daugh - ter, There's
Draw me a buc-ket of wa - ter for my el-dest daugh - ter, There's
Draw me a buc-ket of wa - ter for my el-dest daugh - ter, There's
Draw me a buc-ket of wa - ter for my el-dest daugh - ter, There's

none in the bunch, we're all out the bunch, You go un-der Sis-ter Sal- ly.
one in the bunch, we're three out the bunch, You go un-der Sis-ter Sal- ly.
two in the bunch, we're two out the bunch, You go un-der Sis-ter Sal- ly.
three in the bunch, we're one out the bunch, You go un-der Sis-ter Sal- ly.

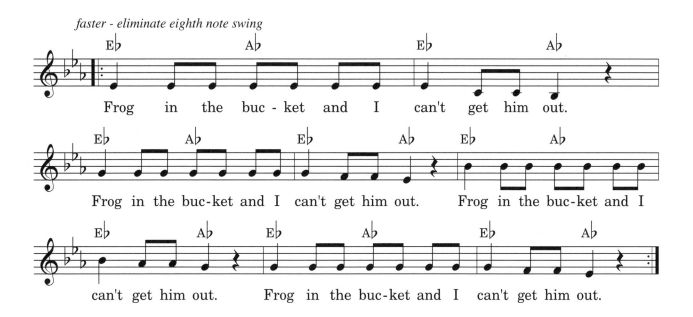

faster - eliminate eighth note swing

Frog in the buc - ket and I can't get him out.

Frog in the buc-ket and I can't get him out. Frog in the buc-ket and I

can't get him out. Frog in the buc-ket and I can't get him out.

Notes: This singing game can be done with several groups of four at a time. Make sure that the rocking is gentle; you can tell the children to stand with one foot forward and one foot back, rocking without lifting either foot off the floor. If they rock too much the whole group might fall over. In the ***Frog in the bucket*** part where they are still a basket you might have the children just bounce up and down gently if turning the basket is too difficult. Then when they undo the basket and have a regular circle holding hands they can jump as vigorously as they want.

Head and Shoulders

John Krumm learned this version from folksinger Bill Dooley. Since then he has found elementary school teachers in Philadelphia who remembered doing this singing game as children.

Head and shoul-ders ba-by, one, ba-by two, ba-by three, Head and
Knees and an - kles ba-by, one, ba-by two, ba-by three, Knees and

shoul-ders ba-by, one, ba-by two, ba-by three, Head and shoul-ders, head and
an - kles ba-by, one, ba-by two, ba-by three, Knees and an - kles, knees and

shoul - ders, head and shoul-ders ba-by, one, ba - by two, ba-bythree.
an - kles, knees and an - kles ba - by, one, ba - by two, ba - by three.

Chorus

Well, I ain't been to 'Fris-co, I ain't been to school, I ain't been to

col - lege, but I ain't no fool, to the front, to the back, to the

si - si - side, to the front, to the back, to the si - si - side.

Formation: Circle, not holding hands, or a Leader facing a group of people scattered through the room.

Head and shoulders baby. . .
Put hands on head, then on shoulders, then clap hands together on the first syllable of each **baby.**
Knees and ankles baby. . .
Touch knees and ankles with both hands or just one knee and one ankle with one hand, then clap as before.
I ain't been to 'Frisco
Point diagonally to the right.

I ain't been to school
  Point diagonally to the left.
I ain't been to college
  Point diagonally to the right.
but I ain't no fool
  Wag finger three times starting on the word ain't.
To the front, to the back, to the si- si- side . . .
  Keeping feet together, take small jumps forward, back and from side to side, following the words.
Throw the ball baby . . . and Milk the cow baby. . .
  Mime the words.
Kick the bucket baby. . .
  Stamp the floor on ***Kick*** and do a small kick forward on bucket.
Around the world baby. . .
  Hands on hips, move hips in a circular motion.

Round de Doo Bop

Jump Jim Joe

This is one of the many singing games and dances we learned at Pinewoods Family Week, the Country Song and Dance Society's summer camp of traditional dance and song. We have since learned that Jump Jim Joe is related to the song 'Jump Jim Crow', made famous by white minstrel show performer Thomas Dartmouth Rice in 1828. The song was so widespread that it gave its name to the "Jim Crow" laws that kept African Americans in subjugation for many years after the abolition of slavery. We have included further information and discussion on this issue on our website: www.dancingmasters.com/JumpJimJoe

While 'Jump Jim Joe' on its own merits is a beautifully simple and engaging singing game, it is certainly understandable to choose not to use it because of its complicated ancestry. One could also say that this is an example of a painful symbol evolving into a positive, community building activity.

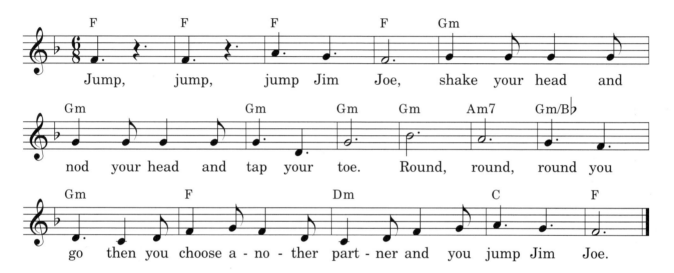

Formation: Couples scattered in no particular order. Partners facing each other and holding both hands with each other.

Jump, jump, jump Jim Joe
Jump five times, once on each of the words.
Shake your head
All shake head from side to side.
and nod your head
All nod head up and down.
and tap your toe.
Still holding partners hands, everyone tap one toe on the floor.
Round, round, round you go
Two hand turn with your partner
then you choose another partner
Everyone drop partner's hands, find another partner, and take two hands with them.
and you jump Jim Joe.
If you have found a new partner in time you jump to the last three words.

Notes: Jump Jim Joe can also be done as a snowball dance, starting with a circle of dancers with no partners around one couple. After the couple in the center has done the dance once through, they each choose a partner from the outer circle. After those two couples dance in the center, they separate and each choose a new partner, again from the outside circle, and so on until all are dancing.

Sometimes we suggest three rules for the singing game: always say yes when asked to dance; odd people out can be included in a threesome; and everyone keep singing the whole time.

Little Johnny Brown

Mary Alice learned this from Jackie Spector's Folk Music Class at the Brookline Arts Center in 1976.
It can be found in the wonderful collection 'Step It Down' by Bessie Jones and Bess Lomax Hawes.

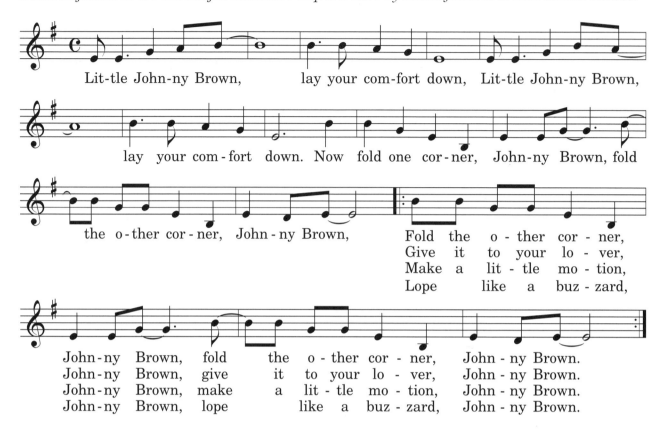

Lit-tle John-ny Brown, lay your com-fort down, Lit-tle John-ny Brown,

lay your com-fort down. Now fold one cor-ner, John-ny Brown, fold

the o-ther cor-ner, John-ny Brown,
Fold the o-ther cor-ner,
Give it to your lo-ver,
Make a lit-tle mo-tion,
Lope like a buz-zard,

John-ny Brown, fold the o-ther cor-ner, John-ny Brown.
John-ny Brown, give it to your lo-ver, John-ny Brown.
John-ny Brown, make a lit-tle mo-tion, John-ny Brown.
John-ny Brown, lope like a buz-zard, John-ny Brown.

Formation: Circle, not holding hands. The Leader is in the center with a folded up square piece of material such as a scarf. This is the 'comfort'.

Little Johnny brown, lay your comfort down, little Johnny Brown, lay your comfort down.
　The Leader lays the comfort down on the floor and spreads it out.
Fold one corner, Johnny Brown . . .
　The Leader folds one corner over after another, following the words of the song.
Give it to your lover, Johnny Brown . . .
　The Leader picks up the folded comfort and hands it to one of the other children in the circle. The Leader stays standing in front of the recipient until they switch places for the next round.
Make a little motion, Johnny Brown . . .
　The Leader makes up a motion that the rest of the children imitate.
Lope like a buzzard, Johnny Brown . . .
　The Leader and everyone else stick thumbs in armpits and flap elbows and move the body like a buzzard to the music of the song.

The child who has received the comfort becomes the Leader for the next time through the game.

Notes: Get yourself a large colorful hankerchief for this one. ***Give it to your friend*** can replace ***Give it to your lover.*** You can use 'Jenny Brown' for girls.

Little Sally Walker

This is our composite of several of the African American versions of 'Little Sally Walker'.
The singing style on the companion recording is influenced by the singing of Bessie Jones.

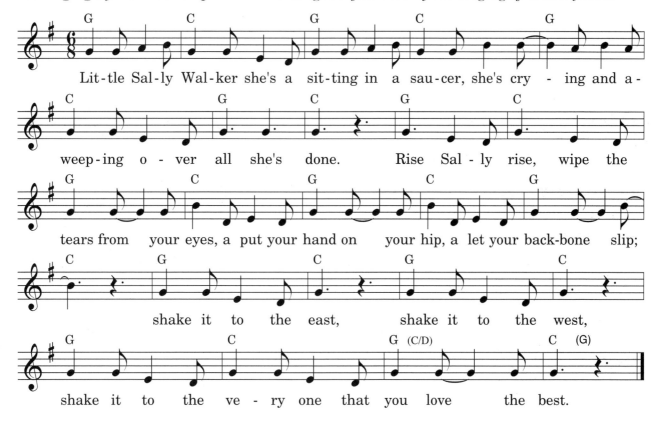

Lit-tle Sal-ly Wal-ker she's a sit-ting in a sau-cer, she's cry - ing and a-

weep-ing o - ver all she's done. Rise Sal - ly rise, wipe the

tears from your eyes, a put your hand on your hip, a let your back-bone slip;

shake it to the east, shake it to the west,

shake it to the ve - ry one that you love the best.

Formation: Circle, all holding hands. Leader in middle of circle.

Little Sally Walker she's a sitting in a saucer, she's a crying and a weeping over all she's done.
All circle to the left around the Leader who crouches in the middle of the circle and mimes crying.

Rise Sally Rise
Stop circling, let go of hands, and all motion with hands for the Leader to rise, and the Leader rises.

wipe the tear from your eyes
All (including Leader) mime wiping away the tear.

put your hand on your hip
All (including Leader) put one hand on one hip or both hands on both hips.

let your backbone slip
All (including Leader) bend forward on the word slip.

shake it to the east
All (including Leader) move hips from side to side in time with underlined words.

shake it to the west
All (including Leader) move hips from side to side in time with underlined words.

shake it to the very one that you love the best.
Dancers in circle move hips from side to side in time with underlined words WHILE the Leader spins around and around covering eyes with one hand and pointing with the other, stopping on the final word **best.** Whomever the Leader is pointing to becomes the new Leader for the next time through the game.

Notes: You can use "Sally Walker" for girls and "Johnny Walker" for boys, or you can use the children's first names, each with the last name "Walker".

The Noble Duke of York

We started using this classic American play party game after dancing it at one of Andy Davis's community dances. We have added a couple of variations that make it more dynamic for older children.

Formation: Longways set of 6-8 couples.

Oh, the nob - le Duke of York, he had ten thou - sand men. He
And when they're up they're up, and when they're down they're down, and
Oh a - hun - ting we will go, a - hun - ting we will go, we'll

marched them up to the top of the hill and he marched them down a - gain.
when they're on - ly half - way up they're nei - ther up nor down.
catch a fox and put/him in a box, and then we'll let him go.

Oh, the noble Duke of York,
> All step forward towards partner

He had ten thousand men,
> All step back to place.

He marched them up to the top of the hill and he marched them down again.
> All dosido partner.

And when they're up they're up,
> Top couple take two hands with partner and start sashaying down the middle WHILE other dancers stand on tiptoes and reach as high as they can.

And when they're down they're down,
> Top couple continues sashaying down middle while other dancers crouch down to the floor.

And when they're only halfway up
> Top couple start sashaying back to the top while other dancers crouch halfway, hands on knees.

They're neither up nor down.
> Top couple continue sashaying up while, on the word ***up,*** other dancers jump up in the air, and, on the word ***down,*** land facing up towards top of the set.

Oh a'hunting we will go, a'hunting we will go, we'll catch a fox and put him in a box, and then we'll let him go. (Sing twice through)
> Top couple lead both lines in a skipping cast off to the bottom of the set. Top couple makes a two hand arch at the bottom. The second couple meet below the arch, take inside ('handy') hands (gent's right hand with lady's left hand) with each other, go under the arch and skip back to place. Other couples follow, each taking one hand with partner as they go under the arch.

The original Top couple stays at the bottom and the song and figures are repeated with a new Top couple.

Notes: This can be done as an a cappella singing game, danced to live musical accompaniment, or danced to the "Noble Duke of York" recording on the companion CD.

Old King Glory

Mary Alice learned this from Doug Lipman in a Cambridge, MA course he taught on traditional songs and singing games for children. Since then we've traced it back to Meg Lippert who learned it from a teacher in the Rudolph Steiner School in New York City who, in turn, had collected it from some children in the streets. Meg originally learned it as "We'll all sing glory to the mountain…" with no reference to a king. Somehow the words got changed to "Old King Glory" and that is that way a lot of people do it now.

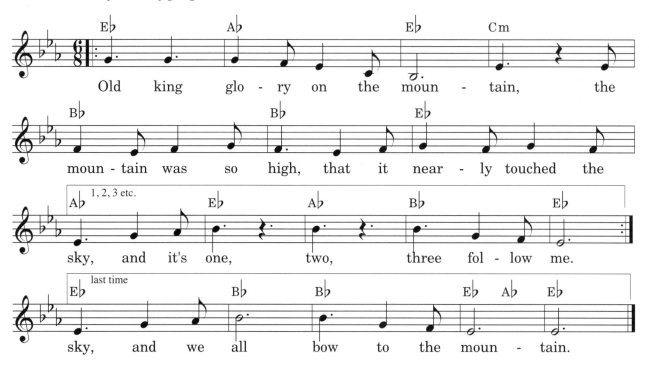

Old king glo - ry on the moun - tain, the
moun - tain was so high, that it near - ly touched the
sky, and it's one, two, three fol - low me.
sky, and we all bow to the moun - tain.

Formation: Circle holding hands. Leader is on the outside of the circle.

All circle left (clockwise) as the Leader walks around the outside of the circle in the opposite direction (counterclockwise).

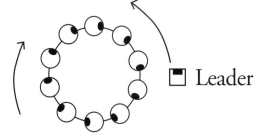

Leader

The Leader taps three adjacent children on the shoulders on the words **one, two, three.** The first two tapped children continue walking in the inner circle, while the child who was tapped on **three** leaves the circle and, with their right hand, takes the Leader's left hand and follows the Leader. The circling inner circle of children continue walking and singing as they close the gap in the circle.

At the next **one, two, three** the same Leader again taps three adjacent children on the shoulder. This third tapped child leaves the circle and, with their right hand, takes the left hand of the child following the leader. Eventually the Leader is leading a long curving line of children counterclockwise around the small and shrinking clockwise circle.

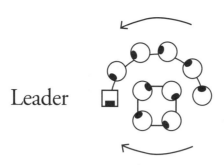

Leader

When there is just one child left in the middle, the Leader takes the left hand of the last person in the line in their right hand to form a circle around the last child in the middle.

Leader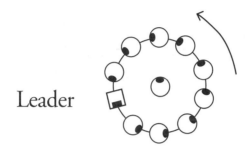

This new outside circle continues moving counterclockwise until the words *touched the sky.* Here the children substitute the last ending: *and we all bow to the mountain* as everyone stops, drops hands, and bows to the child in the middle. This middle child might be the new Leader for another round of Old King Glory or for another game.

Notes: This is a very simple and magical singing game. It might be best to have an adult Leader when first teaching the dance to younger children, but let the children themselves lead it as soon as they are able.

Old Bald Eagle

We learned this version of this American playparty game from Kathy Torrey's recording and booklet of singing games: 'Roots of the Tree of Life'.

Formation: Circle of couples

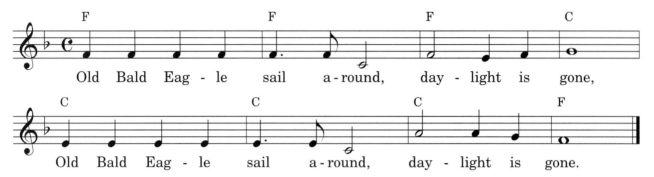

Old Bald Eagle sail around . . .
    Designated Lead Couple promenades to the right (counterclockwise) around the inside of the circle and back to place.

Forward and back across the floor
    All take hands in the circle, go three steps forward and stop.
daylight is gone
    All go back three steps to place.
Forward and back across the floor, daylight is gone.
    All go forward and back again.

You swing yours and I'll swing mine, daylight is gone,
You swing yours and I'll swing mine, daylight is gone.
    All do a two hand turn with partner two or three times around.

Repeat the dance, with couple to the right of the Lead Couple becoming the new Lead Couple.

Notes: The promenading can be walking or skipping, depending on how large the circle is. The promenading couple should get back just in time to join the circle for the forward and back. If you have a very large group, such as in a community dance, you can have two or more couples promenade around at the same time so that everyone gets a turn.

Round de Doo Bop

We learned this version of 'I Was Going to Kentucky' from John Krumm at Family Week at Pinewoods Camp. He'd learned it from some fourth grade girls who danced it as a playground game in the Elkins Park, PA Elementary School.

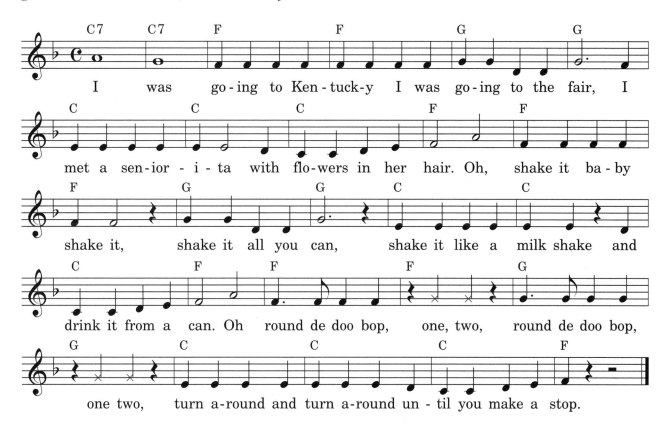

Formation: Circle, all holding hands. Leader in the middle.

I was going to Kentucky I was going to the fair to meet a Seniorita
  Circle to the left
with flowers in her hair
  All stop circling, drop hands, and mime flowers in hair.
Oh shake it baby, shake it, shake it all you can, shake it like a milkshake
  Everyone, including Leader, shakes to the music.
And drink it from a can.
  All mime drinking from a can.
Oh round de doo bop
  Everyone except the Leader spin around once on one foot.
One, two!
  Stamp on one and clap on two.
Round de doo bop, one, two!
  Repeat above spin, stamp and clap.
Turn around and turn around until you make a stop.
  Leader turns around and around while covering eyes with one hand and pointing with the other hand. Leader stops at **stop** and whomever they are pointing to becomes the new Leader.

Sally Go Round the Sun

Mary Alice learned this classic English singing game from Doug Lipman's course on children's music and singing games in Cambridge MA in 1976.

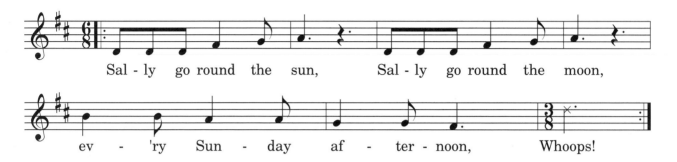

Sal - ly go round the sun, Sal - ly go round the moon,

ev - 'ry Sun - day af - ter - noon, Whoops!

Formation: Circle, all holding hands.

Circle left. At **Whoops!** all jump in the air and circle back to the right. Continue circling to the left and right changing direction at each **Whoops!**.

Notes: Children have a tendency to stop singing after the jump, so we start by teaching only the **Whoops! Sally go round the sun** a few times, connecting the jumping at the end of the song with the walking as the song begins again.

Sally Go Round the Sunshine

At about the same time Mary Alice learned 'Sally Go Round the Sun' she learned this version of the same singing game from children at a primarily African American day care center in Cambridge, MA.

Sal - ly go round the sun - shine, Sal - ly go round the moon,

Sal - ly go round the sun - shine, all on an af - ter - noon, Unh!

Formation: Circle, all holding hands.

Circle left. At **Unh!** all turn in a single motion to face in the opposite direction and circle back to the right. Continue circle to the left and right changing direction at each **Unh!**.

Notes: The **Unh!** is sort of a grunt. You can use this singing game to help develop a dynamic walking step for other traditional dances. Practice moving in the spirit and rhythm of the song as sung on the companion recording.

Skip to My Lou

This was a popular courting game in the Appalachians in the 19th century when dancing was considered a 'wicked sport' and these play parties were considered innocent alternatives.

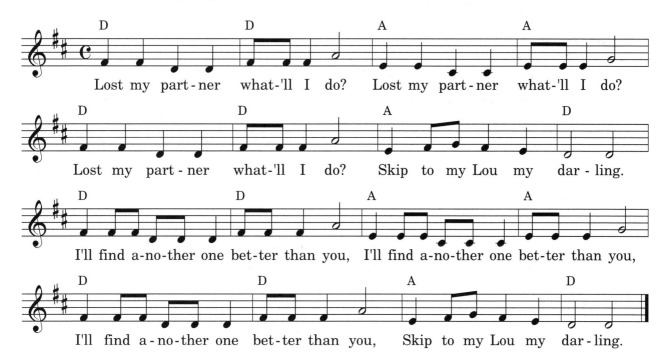

Lost my part-ner what-'ll I do? Lost my part-ner what-'ll I do?

Lost my part-ner what-'ll I do? Skip to my Lou my dar-ling.

I'll find a-no-ther one bet-ter than you, I'll find a-no-ther one bet-ter than you,

I'll find a-no-ther one bet-ter than you, Skip to my Lou my dar-ling.

Formation: Circle of couples, each child holding only their partner's hand. One child is without a partner.

Lost my partner what'll I do . . .

The single child skips around the center of the circle.

I'll find another one better than you . . .

The skipping child 'steals' a partner out of the circle and the two of them skip around the inside of the circle side by side and back to the stolen one's place. The child whose partner had been stolen now becomes the new single child and the dance is repeated.

Notes: A simple variation is to have a circle of children with no partners. Start with a single child skipping around the center while children in the circle clap. At *I'll find another one better than you . . .* that child chooses any of the children in the circle with whom to skip around the center. The next time through the dance the original skipping child joins the circle and the child chosen in the previous round becomes the single child skipping around for the next round of the dance.

Shoo Fly

We learned version II of this American playparty game from Andra Horton at Pinewoods Family Week. We made up the other two versions.

Shoo fly don't bo - ther me, shoo fly don't bo - ther me,

shoo fly don't bo - ther me, for I be - long to some - bo - dy.

I feel, I feel, I feel like a mor - ning star. I

feel, I feel, I feel like a mor - ning star.

Formation: Circle, all holding hands.

LEVEL ONE:

Shoo fly don't both me,
> All take three steps forward, stop on fourth beat.

shoo fly don't bother me,
> All take three steps back to place, stopping on fourth beat.

shoo fly don't bother me, for I belong to somebody.
> Repeat the above forward and back.

I feel, I feel, I feel like a morning star. I feel, I feel, I feel like a morning star.
> All circle to the left

I feel, I feel, I feel like a morning star. I feel, I feel, I feel like a morning star.
> All circle to the right.

LEVEL TWO:

Shoo fly don't both me, shoo fly don't bother me . . .
> All forward and back twice.

I feel, I feel, I feel like a morning star . . .
> A designated Leader, who is part of the circle, leads into the middle and across to the other side of the circle, gently pulling everyone under a two-hand arch on the other side. No one lets go of any hands as everyone follows under the arch. The two dancers holding up the arch go under last, turning under their own arms and the circle is turned inside out. Then all let go of hands and turn to face the center of the circle again, rejoining hands.

LEVEL THREE:

Shoo fly don't both me, shoo fly don't bother me . . .
> All forward and back twice.

I feel, I feel, I feel like a morning star . . .
> Two adjacent dancers are designated Leaders. They lead across the center of the circle walking side by side and gently pulling the rest of the children under a two hand arch made by two dancers on the other side of the circle. After the two Leaders go under the arch they turn back to back under their own two joined hands and pull everyone under their arch as well (so all the dancers are going under two arches). No one lets go of hands throughout, and the circle ends up all facing in as at the beginning of the dance.

Notes: We use Level One as a first dance for younger children. Levels II and III are more sophisticated and magical; they can be used to challenge a group that needs work on cooperation skills.

Thorn Rosa

Versions of this singing play, which originates in Germany, can be found in England and the United States.

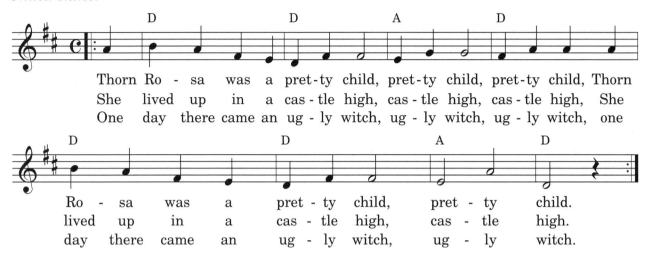

Thorn Ro - sa was a pret-ty child, pret-ty child, pret-ty child, Thorn
She lived up in a cas-tle high, cas-tle high, cas-tle high, She
One day there came an ug - ly witch, ug - ly witch, ug - ly witch, one

Ro - sa was a pret - ty child, pret - ty child.
lived up in a cas - tle high, cas - tle high.
day there came an ug - ly witch, ug - ly witch.

Formation: Two concentric circles around the designated Thorn Rosa. The inside circle is the Castle and the outside circle becomes the Thorny Hedge. The designated Witch and Handsome Prince both start out as part of the Thorny Hedge circle. Children in both circles are holding hands.

Thorn Rosa was a pretty child ...

The Castle circles to the right and the Thorny Hedge circles to the left around Thorn Rosa.

She lived up in a castle high ...

The Thorny Hedge continues circling as the Castle children stop and raise their held hands to look like a castle.

One day there came an ugly witch ...

The Thorny Hedge children stop circling and drop hands as the Witch goes inside the Castle and touches Thorn Rosa on her shoulder. Thorn Rosa immediately swoons to the floor in a deep sleeping trance. The Witch rejoins the Thorny Hedge.

Thorn Rosa Slept a hundred years ...

The Thorny Hedge children slowly crouch down to the floor.

A thorny hedge grew giant high ...

The Thorny Hedge children, making sharp thorns with their fingers, slowly grow to a standing position with arms raised above their heads.

One day there came a handsome prince ...

The Handsome Prince runs (gallops his horse) around the outside of the Thorny Hedge.

He broke right through the thorny hedge . . .

As the Handsome Prince gallops around the outside, he touches each Thorny Hedge child on the back and they respond by dropping their raised "thorny hedge" arms down to their sides.

Thorn Rosa wakened at his touch . . .

The Handsome Prince goes inside the Castle and touches the sleeping Thorn Rosa on the shoulder. Thorn Rosa awakens and stands up.

They all lived for a hundred years . . .

Thorn Rosa and the Handsome Prince take two hands and circle (two hand turn) to the left. The Castle children bring their held hands down and, still holding hands, circle to the right. The Thorny Hedge children take hands again and circle to the left.

Notes: All the children can make ugly faces and use ugly voices in the Ugly Witch verse. Try dropping hands and bowing together on the last *a hundred years.* A variation of this singing game for younger children is to have only one circle around Thorn Rosa that is the Castle on the second verse and later becomes the Thorny Hedge.

When I Was a Baby

We learned this at a workshop of African American singing games led by Penny Schultz.
She'd learned it from a Bess Lomax Hawes video tape of children's games in urban Los Angeles.
Penny had changed it some already, and we changed the teacher's 'Stop!' to 'Help'.

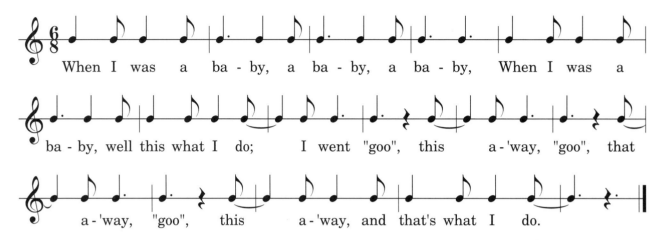

Formation: Circle, not holding hands, or a Leader facing a group scattered through the room.

When I was a baby . . .
   Hands on hips stepping in place to the song.
Now this what I do
   Point, moving index finger up and down.
I went "goo", this a 'way
   Mime thumb sucking to one side.
goo, that a 'way
   Mime thumb sucking to the other side with the other hand.
goo, this a 'way
   Mime to first side again.
And that's what I do.
   Shake index finger as before.

When I went to school, to school, to school, when I went to school, well this what I do
   Same motions as in first verse.
I went JUMP, this a 'way, JUMP that a'way, JUMP, this a'way
   Jump up each time you say the word *JUMP,* facing back and forth from one side
   to the other.
And that's what I do.
   same as in first verse.

The pattern continues with each new motion done first on one side, then the other and then back to the first side:

When I was a teenager... I went "Unh!"

Your interpretation of a cool and detached teenager from side to side.

When I was a teacher... I went "Help"...

Putting out hand, palm up, as if offering or asking for help.

When I was a parent... I went cook...

One arm curves around like a bowl, the other mimes stirring with a spoon. Switch hands and sides each time.

When I was old... I went "Ooh"...

Mime leaning on a cane from side to side.

When I was dead... I went lay...

Hands together beside head, miming going to sleep, from side to side.

When I went to heaven... I went "Shout!"...

Hands up in the air for joy.

Notes: This is a great singing game to do with large groups. We teach the different elements of the dance with the group sitting down, then invite everyone to stand to dance and sing it with us.

Bobolinka

Zodiac

This is our composite of several versions of this singing game, sometimes known as 'Zudio'. We think that the singing game might go back to slavery, where the 'great big man' ('big fat man' in the version we first learned) would be the slave-master, and the 'hump on your back' might refer to how one walks with a big sack of cotton on one's back, or how one walks after a day in the fields.

Formation: Longways formation of any number of partners.

Here we go zodiac . . .
Everyone hold partner's hands: right in right and left in left. Move arms alternating back and forth in time to the music (right arm goes forward while left arm goes back, left arm goes forward while right arm goes back, in a sort of pumping motion).

Step back Sally . . .
Step, or jump back on the first beat of each measure, and clap hands together on the second beat of each measure, moving further and further away from your partner.

Here we go zodiac . . . Step back Sally . . .
Run forward to partner and repeat the above sequence.

Looking down the alley and a'what do I see . . .
Mime shading eyes to look down the middle of the line.

I see a great big man from Tennessee
Mime being a great big man.

I bet you five dollars that you can't do this
Shake index finger.

To the front, to the back, to the si-si-side . .
Keeping feet together make small jumps forward, backward, and side to side, as indicated by the words.

Here we go zodiac . . .
Repeat all the above to the second ending:

You lean way back, you got a hump on your back
Lean back, then lean forward with arched back.

you do the camel's walk, you do the camel's walk . . .
Still leaning forward, you walk forward in step to the music, changing places and sides with partner.

Repeat the entire dance from the other side.

Notes: This is instantly engaging for older elementary students, or for a mixed age community dance.

Here we go zo-di-ac, zo-di-ac, zo - di-ac. Here we go zo-di-ac, all day long.

Step back Sal-ly, Sal-ly, Sal - ly, step back Sal-ly all day long.

Look-ing down the al-ley and a-'what do I see, I see a great big man from

Ten-ne - see. I bet you five dol-lars that you can't do this,

1. to the front, to the back, to the si - si - side, to the front, to the

back, to the si-si - side, to the si-si - side. 2. You lean way back,

you got a hump on your back, you do the ca - mel's walk, you do the

ca-mel's walk, you do the ca-mel's walk, you do the ca-mel's walk.

Glossary

above: Towards the top of a longways set.

arch: Two dancers join one or both hands and raise arms to let other dancers through.

beat: Equivalent to a half measure of music ($\quad$ in $\frac{4}{4}$; $\quad$. in $\frac{6}{8}$). The time needed to take one step. Dance tempo is usually about two beats, or two steps, per second.

below: Towards the bottom of a longways set.

bottom: The end of a longways set where the last couple had lined up.

cast off: Lead couple turn away from each other and walk down the outside of a set. Other dancers follow the lead couple in their lines.

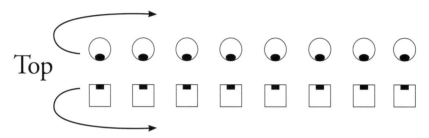

circle formation: Dancers standing side by side in a circle, all facing towards the center.

circle left, circle right: Dancers join hands in a ring and move either to the left (clockwise) or the right (counterclockwise).

clockwise/counterclockwise: Clockwise is the direction the hands of a clock go if the clock is laying face up on the floor; counterclockwise is the opposite direction. For dancers holding hands in a circle, clockwise is the same as circle left, and counterclockwise is the same as circle right.

couple: Two people dancing together.

do-si-do: Literally 'back to back'. Two dancers face each other and walk forward passing right shoulders, then go around each other and back to place. Arms are relaxed at sides throughout.

down: Towards the bottom of a longways set.

first couple: The couple at the top of a longways set. Usually this would be the first couple to line up when forming the set.

forward and back: Step forward three steps and stop, step back three steps and stop.

handy hand: When two dancers are standing side by side, the handy hands are the hands between them: the left hand dancer's (traditional 'gent' side) right hand, and the right hand dancer's (traditional 'lady' side) left hand.

leader: The person chosen to lead the singing game once through; the person who is 'It' in the dance. See the section on Choosing Partners and Leaders.

longways formation: Partners facing each other in two lines. When the line is forming, the first two dancers to line up are designated the first couple, and that end of the line is designated the top of the set. Other couples then line up below them, towards the bottom of the set.

mime: To act something out with motions. When you are miming crying for example, as in Little Sally Walker, you look like you are crying, but instead of making crying noises, you sing along with the rest of the dancers.

partner: The person you are dancing with. see Introduction and Choosing Partners and Leaders.

promenade: Partners side by side, walking forward together and holding hands. They can promenade holding one hand (handy hand) with partner or holding both hands with partner: right hand in right and left hand in left (skating position).

sashay: Galloping or skipping sideways with a partner, while facing partner and holding both of partner's hands.

singing game: A dance accompanied by the singing of the dancers.

snowball dance: A dance that starts with just two dancers dancing together. Then they separate and each chooses another partner so there are two couples dancing. Then the two couples separate and choose other partners so there are four couples, then eight, and so on, until everyone is dancing.

swing: Two dancers take two hands straight across from each other with slightly bent elbows. They walk or skip around and around each other, revolving clockwise (to the left) and balancing their weight. The swing can also be done by partners hooking elbows and walking or skipping around each other, moving clockwise if hooking right elbows, and counterclockwise if hooking left elbows.

top: The end of a longways set where couples first started lining up; the end where the first couple is. See 'longways formation'.

turn: Dancers join specified hands and move around each other once and back to place. Right hand turn and two hand turn are clockwise, left hand turn is counterclockwise.

up: Towards the top of a longways set.

Other Resources

American Orff Schulwerk Association
147 Bell Street, Suite #300, Chagrin Falls, OH 44022 • 440-600-7329
info@aosa.org • aosa.org

The Organization of American Kodaly Educators
10801 National Blvd. Suite 590, Los Angeles, CA 90064 • 310-441-3555
info@oake.org • www.oake.org

The above are two major music teaching organizations, both of which sponsor music teacher conferences and publish singing games collections.

New England Dancing Masters (NEDM)
41 West Street, Brattleboro VT 05301 • 802-257-1819
info@dancingmasters.com • www.dancingmasters.com

Publishers of books, recordings, DVDs and online resources for schools and communities. Here are NEDM's other published collections of singing games:
Down in the Valley - More Great Singing Games for Children (book and companion CD)
I'm Growing Up - Fingerplays, Action Songs, Singing Games and Stories for Young Children (book/CD/DVD)

NEDM has also published several collections (books, CDs and DVDs) of dancing for children and communities.
Andy Davis andy@dancingmasters.com
Mary Cay Brass mcbrass@vermontel.net • www.marycaybrass.com
Peter and Mary Alice Amidon amidonpeter@gmail.com • maryaliceamidon@gmail.com
www.amidonmusic.com

Country Dance and Song Society (CDSS)
116 Pleasant St., Suite 345, Easthampton MA 01027-2759 • 413-203-5467
sales@cdss.org • www.cdss.org

An organization dedicated to traditional dance and song in the United States. CDSS has a superb catalogue of books, CDs and DVDs on traditional dance which you can order by mail or directly by visiting the office. Check out their online catalogue. The singing games collections will show up at www.cdss.org/children-and-community-dance.html

CDSS also sponsors several weekend and week-long dance camps; some specifically for adults, and some for all ages. We learned many of the singing games and dances in our NEDM collections at CDSS summer Family Week Camps. CDSS is a clearinghouse of information about regional dances and traditional dance organizations throughout the United States.

Words to Singing Games

Alabama Gal

Come through in a hurry,
Come through in a hurry,
Come through in a hurry,
Alabama Gal

I don't know how, how, (3X)
Alabama Gal

I'll show you how how, (3X)
Alabama Gal

Ain't I rock candy, (3X)
Alabama Gal

Bobolinka

Forward we go, Bobolinka,
Back we go, Bobolinka,
Forward we go, Bobolinka,
Won't you be my partner.

Two hands around, Bobolinka (3X)
Right back where you started.

Up and down, Bobolinka (3X)
Now you make an alley.

Through the alley, Bobolinka (3X)
Move up one place, start again.

Thorn Rosa

Bulldog

Way down south in the hanky pank,
I say, bulldog, bulldog, hanky pank,
I say, fee, fi, fo, fum,
Listen to that bulldog.

Circle Round the Zero

Circle round the zero,
Find your love in the zero,
Back, back, zero,
Side, side, zero,
Front, front, zero,
Find your love in the zero.

Dinah's Dead

Well, Dinah's dead.
Well how did she die?
Well she died like this.
Well she died like this.
Well, Dinah's dead.
Well how did she die?
Well she died like this.
Well she died like this.
But her sister's still living.
Well, where is she living?
She's living in a place called Tennessee,
With a short, short dress all above her knees.
Hands up, Tizzie Lizzie, Tennessee.
Hands down, Tizzie Lizzie, Tennessee.
Turn around, Tizzie Lizzie, Tennessee.
Touch the ground, Tizzie Lizzie, Tennessee.
Well, she never went to college
And she never went to school,
But when she came back
She was an educated fool.

Draw Me a Bucket of Water

Draw me a bucket of water,
For my eldest daughter,
There's none in the bunch,
We're all out the bunch,
You go under sister Sally.

Draw me a bucket of water,
For my eldest daughter,
There's one in the bunch,
We're three out the bunch,
You go under sister Sally.

Draw me a bucket of water,
For my eldest daughter,
There's two in the bunch,
We're two out the bunch,
You go under sister Sally.

Draw me a bucket of water,
For my eldest daughter,
There's three in the bunch,
We're one out the bunch,
You go under sister Sally.

Frog in the bucket and I can't get him out. (8X)

Head and Shoulders

Head and shoulders baby,
One, baby, two, baby, three.
Head and shoulders baby,
One, baby, two, baby, three.
Head and shoulders
Head and shoulders, head and shoulders baby,
One, baby, two, baby, three.

Knees and ankles baby,
One, baby, two, baby, three.
Knees and ankles baby,
One, baby, two, baby, three.
Knees and ankles
Knees and ankles, Knees and ankles baby,
One, baby, two, baby, three.

Well, I ain't been to Frisco,
I ain't been to school,

I ain't been to college,
But I ain't no fool!
To the front, to the back,
To the si-si-side.
To the front, to the back,
To the si-si-side.

Throw the ball, baby one,
Baby, two, baby three . . .

Milk the cow, baby one,
Baby two, baby three…

Chorus

Kick the bucket,
Baby one, baby two, baby three…

Around the world,
Baby one, baby two, baby three…

Chorus

Jump Jim Joe

Jump, jump, jump, Jim Joe.
Shake your head and nod your head and touch
your toe.
Round, round, round you go
Then you choose another partner
And you jump Jim Joe.

Little Johnny Brown

Little Johnny Brown,
Lay your comfort down,
Little Johnny Brown,
Lay your comfort down.

Fold one corner, Johnny Brown,
Fold another corner, Johnny Brown,
Fold another corner, Johnny Brown,
Fold another corner, Johnny Brown.

Give it to your lover, Johnny Brown (2X)
Make a little motion, Johnny Brown (2X)
Lope like a buzzard Johnny Brown (2X)

Little Sally Walker

Little Sally Walker
She's a'sitting in a saucer,
A'crying and a'weeping over all she's done.
Rise Sally rise, wipe the tear from your eyes,
Put your hand on your hip,
Let your backbone slip,
Shake it to the east, shake it too the west,
Shake it to the very one
That you love the best.

Noble Duke of York

Oh, the noble Duke of York,
He had ten thousand men,
He marched them up to the top of the hill,
And he marched them down again.

And when they're up they're up,
And when they're down they're down.
And when they're only halfway up,
Their neither up nor down.

Oh a'hunting we will go,
A'hunting we will go
We'll catch a fox and
Put him in a box,
And then we'll let him go.

Old Bald Eagle

Old bald eagle sail around,
Daylight is gone
Old bald eagle sail around,
Daylight is gone

Forward and back across the floor,
Daylight is gone,
Forward and back across the floor,
Daylight is gone.

You swing yours and I'll swing mine.
Daylight is gone.
You swing yours and I'll swing mine,
Daylight is gone.

Old King Glory

Old King Glory on the mountain,
The mountain was so high
That it nearly touched the sky,
And it's one, two,
Three follow me.

Round de Doo Bop

I was going to Kentucky,
I was going to the fair,
I met a Seniorita
With flowers in her hair.

Oh, shake it baby, shake it,
Shake it all you can,
Shake it like a milk shake,
And drink it from a can.

Oh, round de doo bop,
One, two!
Round de doo bop,
One, two!
Turn around and turn around
Until you make a stop.

Sally Go Round the Sun

Sally go round the sun,
Sally go round the moon,
All on a Sunday afternoon,
Whoops!

Sally Go Round the Sunshine

Sally go round the sunshine,
Sally go round the moon,
Sally go round the sunshine,
All on an afternoon, unh!

Shoo Fly

Shoo fly, don't bother me,
Shoo fly, don't bother me,
Shoo fly, don't bother me,
For I belong to somebody.

I feel, I feel, I feel like a morning star,
I feel, I feel, I feel like a morning star.
I feel, I feel, I feel like a morning star,
I feel, I feel, I feel like a morning star.

Skip to My Lou

Lost my partner, what'll I do?
Lost my partner, what'll I do?
Lost my partner, what'll I do?
Skip to my Lou my darling.

I'll find another one better than you,
I'll find another one better than you,
I'll find another one better than you,
Skip to my Lou my darling.

Thorn Rosa

Thorn Rosa was a pretty children,
Pretty child, pretty child.
Thorn Rosa was a pretty child,
Pretty child.

She lived up in a castle high,
Castle high, castle high,
She lived up in a castle high,
Castle high.

One day there came an ugly witch . . .
Thorn Rosa slept a hundered years . . .
A thorny hedge grew giant high . . .
One day there came a handsome prince . . .
He broke right through the thorny hedge . . .
Thorn Rosa wakened at his touch . . .
They all lived for a hundred years . . .

When I Was a Baby

When I was a baby,
A baby, a baby,
When I was a baby,
Well this what I do,
I went goo, this a'way,
Goo, that a'way,
Goo, this a'way,
And that's what I do.

When I went to school,
to school, to school,
When I went to school,
Well this what I do,
I went jump, this a'way,
Jump that a'way,
Jump this a'way,
And that's what I do.

When I was a teenager,
A teenager, a teenager,
When I was a teenager,
Well this what I do,

I went "unh" this a'way...

When I was a teacher . . .
I went help this a'way . . .

When I was a parent . . .
I went cook, this a'way . . .

When I was old . . .
I went ooh, this a'way . . .

When I was dead . . .
I went lay this a'way . . .

When I went to heaven . . .
I went Shout! this away . . .

Zodiac

Here we go zodiac, zodiac, zodiac,
Here we go zodiac all day long.
Step back Sally, Sally, Sally
Step back Sally all day long.

Looking down the alley well a'what do I see,
I see a great big man from Tennessee.
I bet you five dollars that you can't do this;
To the front, to the back, to the si-, si-, side;
To the front, to the back, to the si-, si-, side,
To the si-, si-, side.

Here we go Zodiac . . .
I bet you five dollars that you can't do this:
You lean way back,
You got a hump on your back,
You do the camel's walk,
You do the camel's walk,
You do the camel's walk,
You do the camel's walk.

Index of Singing Games by Formation

About the Amidons

Peter and Mary Alice Amidon met at a Ted Sannella contradance in Cambridge, Massachusetts in 1975 where they were swept up in the world of traditional music and dance. Now living in Vermont, they are leaders of traditional dance, song and storytelling in elementary schools, music teacher conferences and music and dance festivals throughout the United States. The Amidons are founding members, along with Andy Davis and Mary Cay Brass, of New England Dancing Masters. The Amidons are also choral arrangers, leaders and publishers. Peter and Mary Alice have two sons, Sam and Stefan, who are both touring musicians.